BASTIEN

CHRISTMAS FOR ADULTS

Sacred and Popular Christmas Carols

Jane Smisor Bastien, Lisa Bastien, & Lori Bastien

Preface

One of the joys of learning to play the piano is the ability to share music with your family and friends. Christmas For Adults is a collection of sacred and popular Christmas classics that have culminated over centuries of musical celebration. We hope you enjoy playing and singing these widely-loved carols for many years to come.

Sincerely,
  Jane Smisor Bastien, Lisa Bastien, and Lori Bastien

This icon is used to indicate on which track of the correlated *Accompaniment Compact Disc* each piece can be found. The circled number inside the icon indicates the particular CD track. Also included is the metronome number at which the accompaniment has been recorded. For those books which are purchased with the *Accompaniment Compact Disc*, the CD is attached inside the back cover. More information about the compact disc may be found on page 2.

(Book plus CD) ISBN 0-8497-7303-2 • (Book only) ISBN 0-8497-7304-0

© 1999 Kjos Music Press, 4380 Jutland Drive, San Diego, California 92117
International copyright secured. All rights reserved. Printed in U.S.A.

About the *Accompaniment Compact Disc*

If this copy of *Bastien Christmas For Adults* was purchased with the compact disc, the CD can be found attached inside the back cover of the book. The *Bastien Christmas For Adults Accompaniment Compact Disc* was created to musically enhance student practice sessions and improve understanding of phrasing, balance, rhythm, and pulse. Each piece in *Bastien Christmas For Adults* includes two CD tracks — one at a slower "practice tempo" and one at a faster "goal tempo" — to facilitate a methodical mastery of the songs. This allows students to use the accompaniments **as they learn** each piece, rather than waiting until the particular challenges of a piece have been mastered.

Each piece on the *Accompaniment Compact Disc* is preceded by a two measure count-off. On the first beat of each count-off measure, a metallic triangle "ding" is heard, followed by wooden stick "clicks" on the remaining beats of the measure. Once the music begins, tempo will vary as dictated by the markings in the music, such as a *ritardando*.

Fermatas appear in the introductions of some pieces. For reasons of timing and ease of playing, these fermatas are **not** observed on the *Accompaniment Compact Disc*. When the CD is used, the student should continue in tempo. When the piano part is played alone or with a partner playing the duet accompaniments included with some pieces, the fermatas can be observed.

On each piece, background accompaniment instruments are heard on the left channel of the recording. The student piano part as it appears in the book is demonstrated on the right channel. The duet accompaniment parts are not heard on the CD. On many sound systems, balance between the left and right channels may be changed, either by adjusting a single "left/right balance control," or by adjusting the volume of the left and right speakers individually. These adjustments allow isolation of either the accompaniment instruments or the student piano part, or modification of the blend between the two.

When first learning a piece, it is recommended that students adjust their sound systems so that the left and right channels are equal, or so that the right channel is favored, allowing the student piano part to be heard as clearly as possible. As students become more proficient playing a piece, it is suggested that they try adjusting their systems to favor the left channel, thus making the student piano part on the right channel very soft or completely silent. This will allow students to play the piano over the accompaniment without the added sound of the demonstration piano coming from the CD.

If using an electronic keyboard, it is important that the pitch of the keyboard match the tuning note found on track 1 of the CD. This tuning note is A above middle C. The reference manual of each particular keyboard should provide information on how to make tuning adjustments.

CONTENTS

JOLLY OLD ST. NICHOLAS

Duet Accompaniment

When played as a duet, the student part is played one octave higher.

JOLLY OLD ST. NICHOLAS

Traditional American Carol

★ The fermatas found here and in other songs are not observed on the *Accompaniment Compact Disc.*

O COME, LITTLE CHILDREN

Duet Accompaniment

When played as a duet, the student part is played one octave higher.

O COME, LITTLE CHILDREN

Music by J. A. P. Schulz
Words by Christoph von Schmid,
Adapted by James Bastien

Moderately

★ A thin double bar line can be used to show the end of a musical section. The end of a section can occur in the middle of a measure, as it does here.

WE WISH YOU A MERRY CHRISTMAS

Duet Accompaniment

When played as a duet, the student part is played one octave higher.

WE WISH YOU A MERRY CHRISTMAS

Traditional English Carol

UP ON THE HOUSETOP
Duet Accompaniment

When played as a duet, the student part is played one octave higher.

UP ON THE HOUSETOP

Words and Music by
Benjamin R. Hanby

JINGLE BELLS

Words and Music by
James S. Pierpont

★ Loco appears after the use of an *8va* to indicate that the music should be played in the octave written.

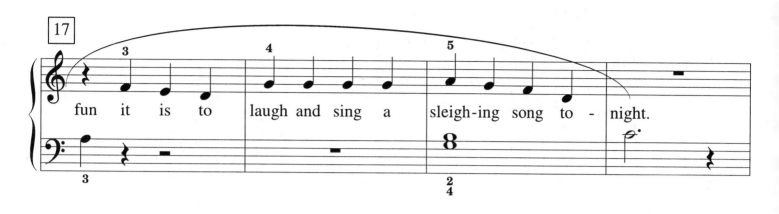

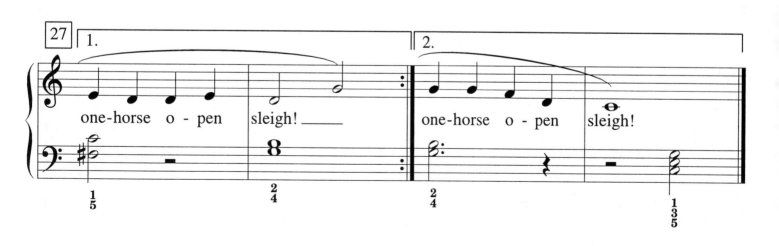

GOOD KING WENCESLAS

Duet Accompaniment

When played as a duet, the student part is played one octave higher.

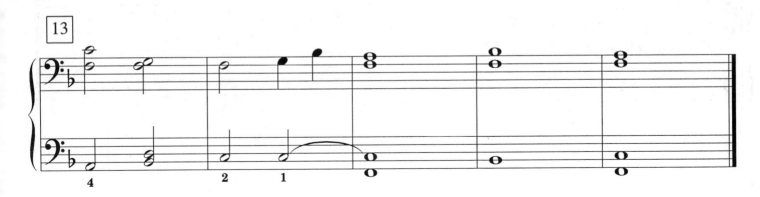

WE THREE KINGS

Words and Music by
John H. Hopkins, Jr.

OH COME, ALL YE FAITHFUL

Duet Accompaniment

When played as a duet, the student part is played one octave higher.

OH COME, ALL YE FAITHFUL

Aderte Fideles

Words and Music by
John Francis Wade,
Translation by Frederick Oakeley

JOY TO THE WORLD

Duet Accompaniment

When played as a duet, the student part is played one octave higher.

JOY TO THE WORLD

Words by Isaac Watts
Music by George F. Handel,
Adapted by Lowell Mason

THE FIRST NOEL

Traditional English Carol

Moderato

The — first —— No - el the — an - gels did say Was to

cer - tain poor shep - herds in fields as they lay; In—

fields —— where — they lay — keep - ing their sheep, On a

24

AWAY IN A MANGER

19th Century American Carol
Music by James Ramsey Murray

KP7

O LITTLE TOWN OF BETHLEHEM

Words by Phillips Brooks
Music by Lewis H. Redner

KP7

ANGELS WE HAVE HEARD ON HIGH

With spirit

Traditional French Carol

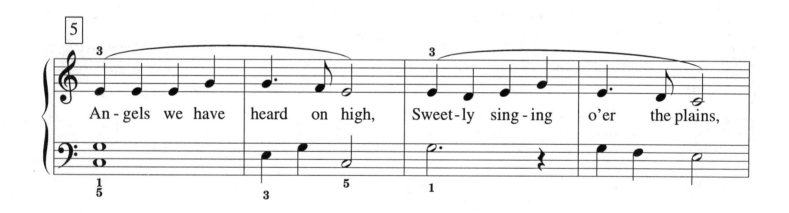

An - gels we have heard on high, Sweet - ly sing - ing o'er the plains,

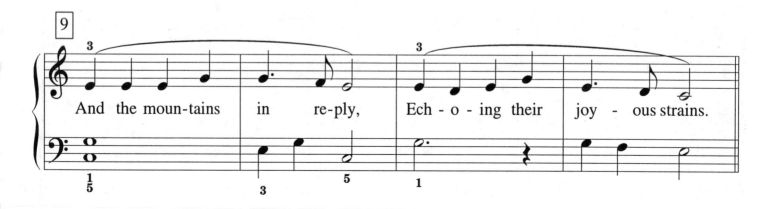

And the moun - tains in re - ply, Ech - o - ing their joy - ous strains.

SILENT NIGHT

Words by Joseph Mohr
Music by Franz Gruber

Andante

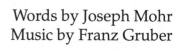

Si - lent night, ho - ly night,

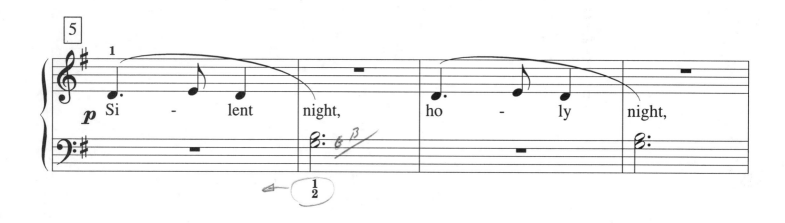

All is calm, all is bright,

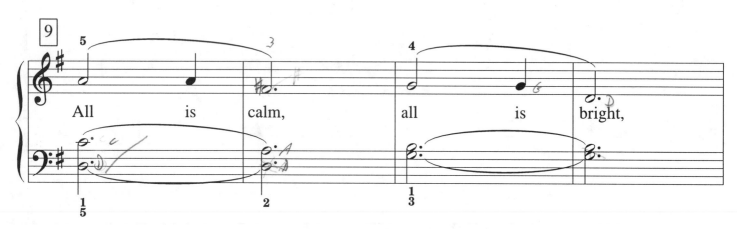

HARK! THE HERALD ANGELS SING

Words by Charles Wesley
Music by Felix Mendelssohn,
Adapted by W. H. Cummings

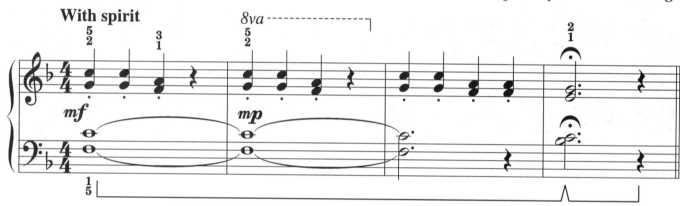

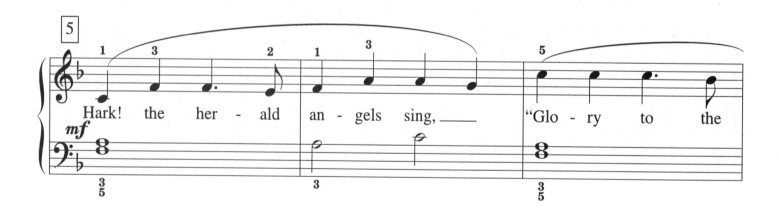

Hark! the her - ald an - gels sing, ___ "Glo - ry to the

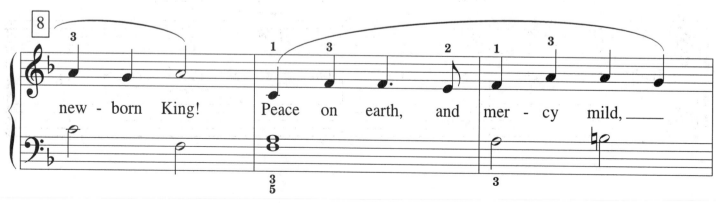

new - born King! Peace on earth, and mer - cy mild, ___

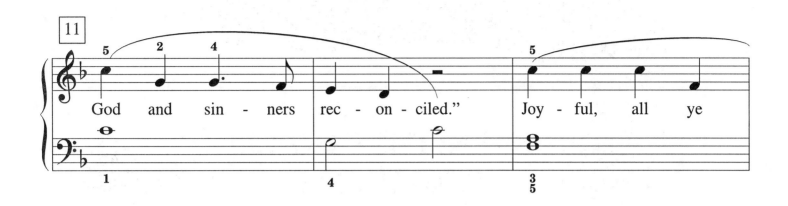

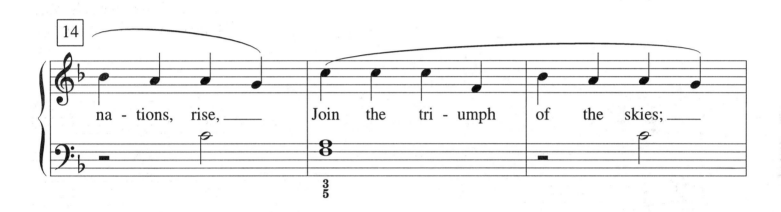

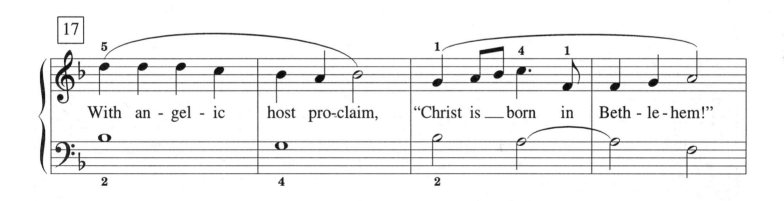

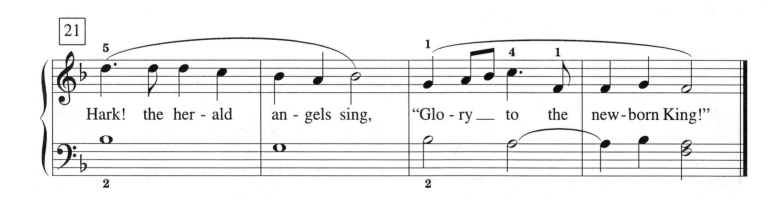

O CHRISTMAS TREE

Traditional German Carol

DECK THE HALL

Traditional American Words
to an Old Welsh Air

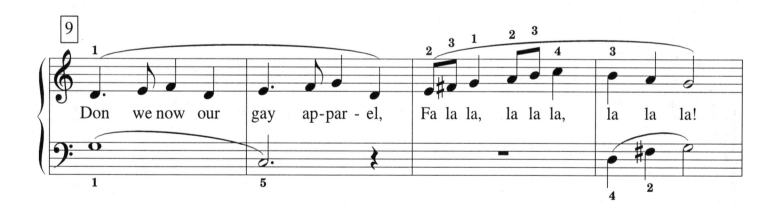

KP7

RUDOLPH THE RED-NOSED REINDEER

Words and Music by
Johnny Marks

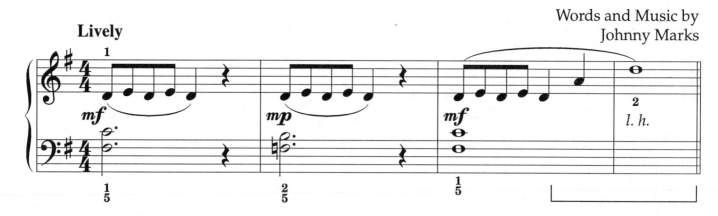

Ru-dolph, the red-nosed reindeer had a ver-y shin - y nose,

And if you ev - er saw it, you would e-ven say it glows.

All of the oth - er reindeer used to laugh and call him names,

A HOLLY JOLLY CHRISTMAS

Words and Music by
Johnny Marks

I'LL BE HOME FOR CHRISTMAS

Words and Music by
Kim Gannon and Walter Kent

I HEARD THE BELLS ON CHRISTMAS DAY

Words by Henry Wadsworth Longfellow
Music by John Baptiste Calkin

Moderato

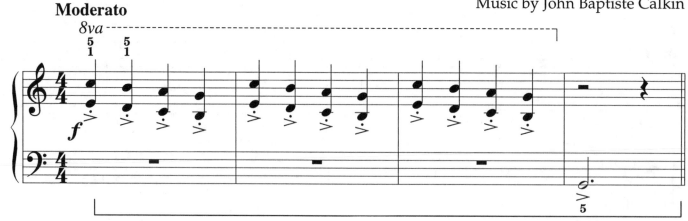

I heard the bells on Christ-mas Day Their old, fa-mil-iar car-ols play, And

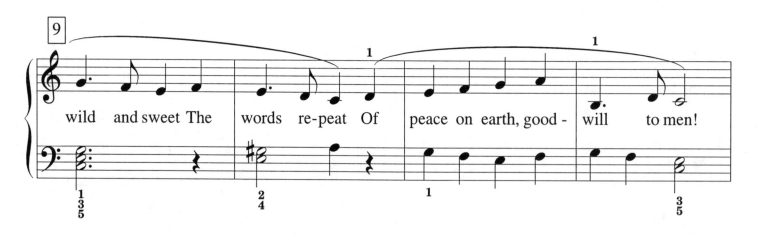

wild and sweet The words re-peat Of peace on earth, good-will to men!

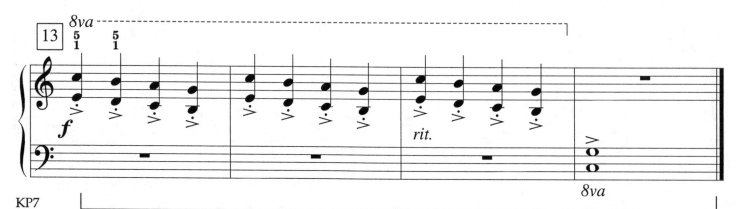

rit.